Scavenger Guides

THE DISNEY WORLD QUEUE LINE SCAVENGER HUNT

THE GAME YOU PLAY
WHILE WAITING IN LINE

Also available:

Scavenger Guides Chicago
Scavenger Guides Washington, DC
Scavenger Guides New York City

Scavenger Guides

THE DISNEY WORLD QUEUE LINE SCAVENGER HUNT

THE GAME YOU PLAY
WHILE WAITING IN LINE

Daniel Ireland

Three Leaf Press

Grand Haven, Michigan

Published by Three Leaf Press
www.threeleafpress.com

Printed in the United States of America

First edition
ISBN: 978-0-9845866-4-6

To Nancy, Megan, and Andrew
for their patience, love, and support

CONTENTS

Searching is half the fun: life is much more manageable when thought of as a scavenger hunt as opposed to a surprise party.

- Jimmy Buffett

CHAPTER 1

GAME ON!

*T*he *Disney World Queue Line Scavenger Hunt* will help you pass the time while waiting in line at the Walt Disney World Resort. It's a great way to turn waiting in queue lines into an adventure and add fun to your visit!

Almost all of the items in this scavenger hunt can be found from the queue lines at attractions in the Magic Kingdom, Epcot, Hollywood Studios, and Animal Kingdom. A few attractions, such as the pavilions in Epcot's World Showcase, do not require a waiting period, but have been included to add an additional level of fun while visiting these areas. Some items are easy to find, while others may pose more of a challenge. Unless otherwise noted, scavenger items inside attractions have been avoided as to not distract from your ride experience.

PLAYING THE GAME

Before visiting the parks, decide if you are going to play as individuals or as teams. Families with younger children may wish to play as teams, pairing up an adult or teen with a younger child. Adults and families with older children may choose to play individually or in groups.

Each scavenger item includes a scoring grid for up to six teams. Each team or individual should decide on a team name. Write the name of each team, along with the names of team members, on the following page.

FORMING TEAMS

Write the name of each team, along with the names of team members, below.

(A) Team Name_____

Members _____

(B) Team Name_____

Members _____

(C) Team Name_____

Members _____

(D) Team Name_____

Members _____

(E) Team Name_____

Members _____

(F) Team Name_____

Members _____

SCORING

Note the letter before your team name in the grid for tallying your score during the hunt. While waiting in a long queue, use the table of contents in the front of this book to locate the page that corresponds to that attraction. Find as many of the items on your scavenger hunt as you can. Keep track of your score by marking your team bubble below each item found.

HELPFUL HINTS

Here are some suggestions to help you in your search:

✔ All items can be seen from the queue lines unless otherwise noted.

✔ Items are often listed in the order in which they appear in the queue.

✔ Both easy and hard to find items have been included for each attraction. When teaming, allow younger children to find the more obvious items (marked with an asterisk*) while adults focus on finding the more difficult ones.

✔ When asked to find Mickey, it is often a Hidden Mickey you are looking for. Only well-defined, primarily classic Hidden Mickeys have been included in this scavenger hunt.

✔ If teams separate, you may wish to require photo evidence of items found.

✔ For added fun and excitement, consider rewarding the winning team - perhaps a sweet snack, a souvenir, or dinner at a restaurant of their choice. Be creative!

WHEN YOU FINISH

After you have found as many items as you can, add up all the points from the park for each team. There is a handy worksheet at the end of each section to help you with this task.

At the end of your Disney vacation, add up each team's total points using the worksheet at the end of the book. Compare your total score with the other teams. Who will be crowned *The Disney World Queue Line Scavenger Hunt* grand champion?

Have fun on your Walt Disney World scavenger hunt!

CHAPTER 2

MAGIC KINGDOM

When many people think of Disney World, they picture Cinderella Castle and the Magic Kingdom. The Magic Kingdom was the first park built at the Walt Disney World Resort, opening in 1971. For many people, it is still their favorite park. This also makes it one of the most crowded parks in the Walt Disney World Resort. In 2010, the park hosted over 17 million visitors, making it the most visited theme park in the world.

The Magic Kingdom is divided into six themed lands, arranged like a wheel with the hub in front of Cinderella Castle. Pathways lead from the castle to Tomorrowland, Fantasyland, Frontierland, Liberty Square, Adventureland, and Main Street U.S.A., with the Walt Disney World Railroad running along the perimeter. Currently, Disney lists over 30 attractions in the Magic Kingdom.

Most of the attractions in the Magic Kingdom are traditional rides with winding queues. Some of the queues, such as those outside the Haunted Mansion and The Many Adventures of Winnie the Pooh, have received makeovers recently, making them more interactive and visually appealing. The majority of the scavenger hunt items in the Magic Kingdom can be found in or around the queues. In a few instances where wait times are not required, items can be found directly on the attraction. These include the Liberty Square Riverboat, Swiss Family Treehouse, Tom Sawyer Island, Tomorrowland Transit Authority PeopleMover, and Walt Disney's Carousel of Progress.

ASTRO ORBITER

Prepare to board an Astro Orbiter rocket for a flight high over Tomorrowland! All items on this hunt can be seen from the ground-level queue before boarding the elevator.

1 Find a phone booth.*

Team A ◯   Team B ◯   Team C ◯

Team D ◯   Team E ◯   Team F ◯

2 Find the planet Venus.

Team A ◯   Team B ◯   Team C ◯

Team D ◯   Team E ◯   Team F ◯

3 Find a yellow gear.

Team A ◯   Team B ◯   Team C ◯

Team D ◯   Team E ◯   Team F ◯

4 Find a Coca-Cola meteor.

Team A ◯   Team B ◯   Team C ◯

Team D ◯   Team E ◯   Team F ◯

1. *There is a Metrophone near the elevators.*
2. *On the Merchant of Venus shop sign.*
3. *At the top of the sign for Walt Disney's Carousel of Progress.*
4. *On the Cool Zone sign.*

BIG THUNDER MOUNTAIN RAILROAD

Board a runaway train for a fast, twisting roller coaster ride through a gold mine in the Old West. Items can be found both outside and inside along the queue as it winds through the old mining town.

❶ Find a steer skull.*

Team A ⬭ Team B ⬭ Team C ⬭

Team D ⬭ Team E ⬭ Team F ⬭

❷ Find a crate of "Lytum & Hyde" explosives.

Team A ⬭ Team B ⬭ Team C ⬭

Team D ⬭ Team E ⬭ Team F ⬭

❸ Find a barrel of horseshoes.

Team A ⬭ Team B ⬭ Team C ⬭

Team D ⬭ Team E ⬭ Team F ⬭

❹ Find a crate of Irish Blend whiskey.

Team A ⬭ Team B ⬭ Team C ⬭

Team D ⬭ Team E ⬭ Team F ⬭

1. *At the beginning of the outside queue on the left.*
2. *In the outside queue on the right before the wagons.*
3. *About halfway through the inside queue on a high shelf on the left.*
4. *A crate of Overdigums Irish Blend sits in the rafters over the loading area.*

Buzz Lightyear's Space Ranger Spin

Help Buzz Lightyear fight the evil emperor Zurg and save the universe on this popular Tomorrowland attraction. As you wait to begin your mission, look for these scavenger hunt items along the brightly themed indoor queue.

1 Find an alien plugging its ears.

Team A ◯   Team B ◯   Team C ◯

Team D ◯   Team E ◯   Team F ◯

2 Find a square planet.

Team A ◯   Team B ◯   Team C ◯

Team D ◯   Team E ◯   Team F ◯

3 Find a View-Master.*

Team A ◯   Team B ◯   Team C ◯

Team D ◯   Team E ◯   Team F ◯

4 Find Mickey in a planet.

Team A ◯   Team B ◯   Team C ◯

Team D ◯   Team E ◯   Team F ◯

1. *In the first poster on the right showing Buzz Lightyear's rocket taking off.*
2. *In Sector 5 in the Planets of the Galactic Alliance poster on the wall.*
3. *Near the end of the queue before the giant talking Buzz Lightyear.*
4. *A Hidden Mickey profile appears as a green land mass on a planet twice in the queue - in Sector 1 in the planet poster and to the left of the large View-Master.*

COUNTRY BEAR JAMBOREE

This Frontierland musical show features singing and dancing animatronic bears. Begin your hunt in the lobby of Grizzly Hall. Search for additional items in the theatre as you wait for the show to begin.

1 Find claw marks.

Team A ◯	Team B ◯	Team C ◯
Team D ◯	Team E ◯	Team F ◯

2 Find a raccoon.*

Team A ◯	Team B ◯	Team C ◯
Team D ◯	Team E ◯	Team F ◯

3 Find an owl.

Team A ◯	Team B ◯	Team C ◯
Team D ◯	Team E ◯	Team F ◯

4 Find a small tree with a tall tree.

Team A ◯	Team B ◯	Team C ◯
Team D ◯	Team E ◯	Team F ◯

1. *On the floor of the Grizzly Hall waiting area queue.*
2. *In the painting of the bear playing a guitar in the waiting area queue.*
3. *Under the portrait of Ursus H. Bear above the center stage.*
4. *On the left and right sides of the center stage.*

DUMBO THE FLYING ELEPHANT

Dumbo is one of Fantasyland's original attractions, and it remains one of the most popular rides for younger visitors. Its sparse queue overlooks the heart of Fantasyland, where you can find all of these items.

1 Find an elephant-shaped bush.

Team A ◯   Team B ◯   Team C ◯

Team D ◯   Team E ◯   Team F ◯

2 Find Pinocchio.

Team A ◯   Team B ◯   Team C ◯

Team D ◯   Team E ◯   Team F ◯

3 Find a mouse on a balloon.*

Team A ◯   Team B ◯   Team C ◯

Team D ◯   Team E ◯   Team F ◯

4 Find a pyramid of elephants.

Team A ◯   Team B ◯   Team C ◯

Team D ◯   Team E ◯   Team F ◯

4.   On the lamp posts surrounding the attraction.
3.   On a hot air balloon at the top center of the ride.
2.   Holding a mug and a plate of cake over the Pinocchio Village Haus Restaurant.
1.   The topiary in front of the attraction.

THE HALL OF PRESIDENTS

Conduct your hunt in the lobby of the theater before learning about the history of the United States and its presidents at this Liberty Square show.

❶ Find a president wearing a watch.

Team A ⬭   Team B ⬭   Team C ⬭

Team D ⬭   Team E ⬭   Team F ⬭

❷ Find a fishing reel.*

Team A ⬭   Team B ⬭   Team C ⬭

Team D ⬭   Team E ⬭   Team F ⬭

❸ Find Thomas Jefferson's tooth.

Team A ⬭   Team B ⬭   Team C ⬭

Team D ⬭   Team E ⬭   Team F ⬭

❹ Find Mickey with George Washington.

Team A ⬭   Team B ⬭   Team C ⬭

Team D ⬭   Team E ⬭   Team F ⬭

1. *In his portrait, Ronald Reagan's watch can be seen peaking out from under his shirtsleeve.*

2. *Herbert Hoover's fly fishing reel inside a glass display case.*

3. *Thomas Jefferson's fossilized mastodon tooth behind a glass display case.*

4. *On the back wall, in the large painting of George Washington addressing a crowd, the sword in the center of the painting has a classic Hidden Mickey at its tip.*

THE HAUNTED MANSION

The Haunted Mansion's queue is almost as much fun as the ride itself! Explore the front grounds of the mansion as you search for the items below. Be sure to go left when the line splits to enter the interactive queue.

❶ Find a large raven with shimmering red eyes.

Team A ⬭   Team B ⬭   Team C ⬭

Team D ⬭   Team E ⬭   Team F ⬭

❷ Find a one-eyed cat.

Team A ⬭   Team B ⬭   Team C ⬭

Team D ⬭   Team E ⬭   Team F ⬭

❸ Find a leaky bathtub.*

Team A ⬭   Team B ⬭   Team C ⬭

Team D ⬭   Team E ⬭   Team F ⬭

❹ Find Madame Leota's eye-opening headstone.

Team A ⬭   Team B ⬭   Team C ⬭

Team D ⬭   Team E ⬭   Team F ⬭

1. *Above the organ pipes on the composer crypt in the graveyard.*
2. *In the lower corner of the musical wall on the composer crypt.*
3. *The top section of the sea captains crypt.*
4. *Near the entrance of the Haunted Mansion.*

It's a Small World

Take a ride through the six populated continents of the world as audio-animatronic dolls serenade you. As you wait to board your boat, scan the covered queue that overlooks the attraction's facade to find these items.

1 Find an hourglass.

Team A ◯   Team B ◯   Team C ◯
Team D ◯   Team E ◯   Team F ◯

2 Find a bell.*

Team A ◯   Team B ◯   Team C ◯
Team D ◯   Team E ◯   Team F ◯

3 Find a crown.

Team A ◯   Team B ◯   Team C ◯
Team D ◯   Team E ◯   Team F ◯

4 Find a parade of dolls.

Team A ◯   Team B ◯   Team C ◯
Team D ◯   Team E ◯   Team F ◯

1. *To the right of the clock face above the loading area.*
2. *At the bottom left corner of the clock tower in the loading queue.*
3. *At the base of the flag poles on top of the buildings to the left and right of the clock tower.*
4. *Emerging from the clock tower doors each quarter hour.*

JUNGLE CRUISE

The Jungle Cruise takes you on an adventure down the major rivers of Africa, Asia, and South America. Keep a sharp eye out for the items below as you enter the queue on the loading dock of the Jungle Navigation Company.

1 Find a bicycle with no wheels.*

Team A ◯   Team B ◯   Team C ◯

Team D ◯   Team E ◯   Team F ◯

2 Find a blue teapot.

Team A ◯   Team B ◯   Team C ◯

Team D ◯   Team E ◯   Team F ◯

3 Find a crate of mosquitoes.

Team A ◯   Team B ◯   Team C ◯

Team D ◯   Team E ◯   Team F ◯

4 Find a float plane.

Team A ◯   Team B ◯   Team C ◯

Team D ◯   Team E ◯   Team F ◯

4. *At the top of the Aero Casablanca map near the loading area.*

3. *On the ground near the loading area.*

2. *Atop a crate on a high shelf to the left in the inside queue.*

1. *In a caged enclosure on the right near the beginning of the inside queue.*

LIBERTY SQUARE RIVERBOAT

The Liberty Square Riverboat boards at the dock on the Liberty Square waterfront. Since there is no real queue for this ride, the items below can be seen from the decks of the Liberty Belle as you circle around Tom Sawyer Island.

1 Find a pulley.

Team A ⭕   Team B ⭕   Team C ⭕

Team D ⭕   Team E ⭕   Team F ⭕

2 Find a rooster weathervane.

Team A ⭕   Team B ⭕   Team C ⭕

Team D ⭕   Team E ⭕   Team F ⭕

3 Find a coffee pot.

Team A ⭕   Team B ⭕   Team C ⭕

Team D ⭕   Team E ⭕   Team F ⭕

4 Find a clothesline with laundry.*

Team A ⭕   Team B ⭕   Team C ⭕

Team D ⭕   Team E ⭕   Team F ⭕

1. *Over the sign on Harpers Mill.*
2. *On top of the windmill.*
3. *On a barrel in front of Alligator Swamp.*
4. *In the bushes by Wilsons Cave.*

MAD TEA PARTY

This Alice in Wonderland-themed ride is one of the original Magic Kingdom attractions. Although its queue is basic, it overlooks much of Fantasyland. Look near and far to find the items below.

1 Find a bush shaped like a table.

Team A ◯   Team B ◯   Team C ◯

Team D ◯   Team E ◯   Team F ◯

2 Find a mouse in a teapot.*

Team A ◯   Team B ◯   Team C ◯

Team D ◯   Team E ◯   Team F ◯

3 Find four checkered flags.

Team A ◯   Team B ◯   Team C ◯

Team D ◯   Team E ◯   Team F ◯

4 Find a backwards "S".

Team A ◯   Team B ◯   Team C ◯

Team D ◯   Team E ◯   Team F ◯

1. *In the Alice in Wonderland topiary in front of the attraction.*
2. *The Dormouse can be seen popping his head out of a large teapot in the middle of the ride.*
3. *In the Tomorrowland Speedway attraction next door.*
4. *On the side of one of the cups as well as the large teapot in the middle of the ride.*

THE MAGIC CARPETS OF ALADDIN

Swoop and soar on a magical, flying carpet above Adventureland. The items below can all be seen from the shaded queue that surrounds the attraction..

1 Find a tiger.

Team A ⬭   Team B ⬭   Team C ⬭

Team D ⬭   Team E ⬭   Team F ⬭

2 Find a blue teardrop-shaped jewel.

Team A ⬭   Team B ⬭   Team C ⬭

Team D ⬭   Team E ⬭   Team F ⬭

3 Find a spitting camel.*

Team A ⬭   Team B ⬭   Team C ⬭

Team D ⬭   Team E ⬭   Team F ⬭

3. A large one on the far side of the ride as well as smaller ones along the base.

2. Embedded in the ground near the end of the queue.

1. On the front of the magic carpets.

THE MANY ADVENTURES OF WINNIE THE POOH

Before boarding your honeypot, search the Hundred Acre Wood in this interactive queue to find the items below. Make sure to stop at Rabbit's Garden and explore the Kids Play area.

❶ Find the Nautilus submarine from 20,000 Leagues Under the Sea.

Team A ◯   Team B ◯   Team C ◯

Team D ◯   Team E ◯   Team F ◯

❷ Find a gopher in a hole.*

Team A ◯   Team B ◯   Team C ◯

Team D ◯   Team E ◯   Team F ◯

❸ Find Piglet in a wall of honey.

Team A ◯   Team B ◯   Team C ◯

Team D ◯   Team E ◯   Team F ◯

❹ Find Volume H.

Team A ◯   Team B ◯   Team C ◯

Team D ◯   Team E ◯   Team F ◯

1. *In the woodwork above the door frame inside Mr. Sanders' tree at the beginning of the queue.*
2. *Emerging out of the hole in Rabbit's Garden when the rope is pulled.*
3. *Piglet is hidden behind the honey in the last honey wall on the right.*
4. *On a book in the lower left of the loading area.*

MICKEY'S PHILHARMAGIC

Get ready to enjoy the PhilharMagic Orchestra under the direction of Maestro Mickey Mouse. These items can all be found in the lobby of the Royal Fantasyland Concert Hall before entering the show.

❶ Find a set of maracas.

Team A ◯   Team B ◯   Team C ◯

Team D ◯   Team E ◯   Team F ◯

❷ Find a pig playing a flute.*

Team A ◯   Team B ◯   Team C ◯

Team D ◯   Team E ◯   Team F ◯

❸ Find the entrance for musicians only.

Team A ◯   Team B ◯   Team C ◯

Team D ◯   Team E ◯   Team F ◯

❹ Find Mickey in the wall mural.

Team A ◯   Team B ◯   Team C ◯

Team D ◯   Team E ◯   Team F ◯

1. *In the Festival Mariachis poster.*
2. *In the Wolf Gang Trio poster.*
3. *The gate with the trumpet at the beginning of the queue.*
4. *Several classic Hidden Mickeys can be found in the splatters of white paint.*

MONSTERS, INC. LAUGH FLOOR

As you wait to enter this interactive comedy show, search for these items throughout the winding factory queue as well as in the pre-show area before you enter the theater.

❶ Find an eject button.

Team A ⃝   Team B ⃝   Team C ⃝

Team D ⃝   Team E ⃝   Team F ⃝

❷ Find a note from Dr. Harvey Furrystein, Monstropolis.

Team A ⃝   Team B ⃝   Team C ⃝

Team D ⃝   Team E ⃝   Team F ⃝

❸ Find a can of Blort.*

Team A ⃝   Team B ⃝   Team C ⃝

Team D ⃝   Team E ⃝   Team F ⃝

❹ Find the "Scarer of the Month" sign.

Team A ⃝   Team B ⃝   Team C ⃝

Team D ⃝   Team E ⃝   Team F ⃝

PETER PAN'S FLIGHT

Take a high-flying trip over London and Never Land with Peter Pan and the Darling children. Before boarding your pirate ship, search for the items below in the winding queue.

1 Find a horn.*

Team A ◯ Team B ◯ Team C ◯

Team D ◯ Team E ◯ Team F ◯

2 Find a heart-shaped flower.

Team A ◯ Team B ◯ Team C ◯

Team D ◯ Team E ◯ Team F ◯

3 Find Mickey on a tree.

Team A ◯ Team B ◯ Team C ◯

Team D ◯ Team E ◯ Team F ◯

4 Find a skull and crossbones.

Team A ◯ Team B ◯ Team C ◯

Team D ◯ Team E ◯ Team F ◯

1. *Mounted on the wall on the right side of the queue.*
2. *On both sides of the stroller parking entrance across from Peter Pan's Flight.*
3. *A classic Hidden Mickey can be found on the trunk of the tree where the Fastpass line meets the standby line.*
4. *On the pirate ship's flag in the loading area mural.*

PIRATES OF THE CARIBBEAN

It's a pirates life for all on this classic Disney attraction. Search for the following items throughout the themed queue which winds through the Spanish fort Castillo Del Morro.

1 Find a candlestick.

Team A ⬭   Team B ⬭   Team C ⬭

Team D ⬭   Team E ⬭   Team F ⬭

2 Find a Mickey-shaped lock.

Team A ⬭   Team B ⬭   Team C ⬭

Team D ⬭   Team E ⬭   Team F ⬭

3 Find two skeletons playing chess.

Team A ⬭   Team B ⬭   Team C ⬭

Team D ⬭   Team E ⬭   Team F ⬭

4 Find a cannon hanging from a rope.*

Team A ⬭   Team B ⬭   Team C ⬭

Team D ⬭   Team E ⬭   Team F ⬭

1. *On top of The Pirates League barrel in the outside covered queue.*
2. *On a case of guns in the left queue.*
3. *At the bottom of a dungeon cell in the right queue.*
4. *At two points along the inside queue.*

PRINCE CHARMING REGAL CARROUSEL

One of the few attractions not designed by Disney Imagineers, this 1917 carrousel was once part of an amusement park in New Jersey. Can you spot these items on the carrousel as you wait your turn to ride?

❶ Find a pumpkin.*

Team A ⬭   Team B ⬭   Team C ⬭

Team D ⬭   Team E ⬭   Team F ⬭

❷ Find an Indian.

Team A ⬭   Team B ⬭   Team C ⬭

Team D ⬭   Team E ⬭   Team F ⬭

❸ Find a horse with a golden bow on its tail.

Team A ⬭   Team B ⬭   Team C ⬭

Team D ⬭   Team E ⬭   Team F ⬭

❹ Find a lion.

Team A ⬭   Team B ⬭   Team C ⬭

Team D ⬭   Team E ⬭   Team F ⬭

1. *On the fairy godmother mural at the top of the carrousel.*

2. *On the saddle of a white horse.*

3. *On the white horse said to be Cinderella's horse.*

4. *On the shield of the white horse wearing a green helmet.*

SNOW WHITE'S SCARY ADVENTURES

Enter the world of Snow White and the Seven Dwarfs as you ride through scenes from the 1937 Disney film. The items below can all be found from the often lengthy queue line.

❶ Find a pink jewel.

Team A ◯   Team B ◯   Team C ◯

Team D ◯   Team E ◯   Team F ◯

❷ Find a clothesline.*

Team A ◯   Team B ◯   Team C ◯

Team D ◯   Team E ◯   Team F ◯

❸ Find Mickey on a chimney.

Team A ◯   Team B ◯   Team C ◯

Team D ◯   Team E ◯   Team F ◯

❹ Find a turtle.

Team A ◯   Team B ◯   Team C ◯

Team D ◯   Team E ◯   Team F ◯

1. *Embedded in the ceiling of the Seven Dwarfs Mine to the right of the queue.*
2. *To the left of the house in the loading area mural.*
3. *A classic Hidden Mickey formed by three gray stones below the two flowers on the chimney in the loading area mural.*
4. *In the loading area mural next to the seven dwarfs.*

SPACE MOUNTAIN

This indoor, outer space-themed roller coaster was recently refurbished, including extensive additions to the queue. There is much more to look at, which makes the items below even more difficult to find!

❶ Find a moon orbiting a planet.*

Team A ⬭ Team B ⬭ Team C ⬭

Team D ⬭ Team E ⬭ Team F ⬭

❷ Find Ariel.

Team A ⬭ Team B ⬭ Team C ⬭

Team D ⬭ Team E ⬭ Team F ⬭

❸ Find an astronaut on a moon walk.

Team A ⬭ Team B ⬭ Team C ⬭

Team D ⬭ Team E ⬭ Team F ⬭

❹ Find a rotating space station.

Team A ⬭ Team B ⬭ Team C ⬭

Team D ⬭ Team E ⬭ Team F ⬭

1. *In a window on the right side of the queue.*
2. *A planet on the Triton Stations - Sector Three diagram.*
3. *In a window on the right side of the queue.*
4. *On the ceiling over the loading queue.*

SPLASH MOUNTAIN

This popular Frontierland log flume ride is based on the characters, stories, and songs from the 1946 Disney film Song of the South. Look for the following items along the attraction's lengthy queue.

1 Find a butter churn.

Team A ⬭   Team B ⬭   Team C ⬭

Team D ⬭   Team E ⬭   Team F ⬭

2 Find a blue pot on a yellow table.

Team A ⬭   Team B ⬭   Team C ⬭

Team D ⬭   Team E ⬭   Team F ⬭

3 Find a frog in a rocking chair.*

Team A ⬭   Team B ⬭   Team C ⬭

Team D ⬭   Team E ⬭   Team F ⬭

4 Find a bait box.

Team A ⬭   Team B ⬭   Team C ⬭

Team D ⬭   Team E ⬭   Team F ⬭

1. *In the old barn at the beginning of the queue.*
2. *On the porch of a log cabin birdhouse near the beginning of the queue.*
3. *A silhouette of Brer Frog can be see projected on a screen in his cave home on the left side in the queue.*
4. *In the picture of Brer Goose shortly before the loading area.*

STITCH'S GREAT ESCAPE!

Get up close and personal with the alien Stitch from the Disney film Lilo & Stitch in this Tomorrowland attraction. Although its queue is sparse, you can spot these items if you look closely.

❶ Find a Sleepless Knights sign.*

Team A ⬭   Team B ⬭   Team C ⬭

Team D ⬭   Team E ⬭   Team F ⬭

❷ Find a Dipper Deluxe rocket.

Team A ⬭   Team B ⬭   Team C ⬭

Team D ⬭   Team E ⬭   Team F ⬭

❸ Find a woman holding a baby.

Team A ⬭   Team B ⬭   Team C ⬭

Team D ⬭   Team E ⬭   Team F ⬭

1. On the Tomorrowland sign next to the queue area.
2. On the Antique Rocket Show poster at the back of the queue.
3. On the Space Home & Garden Show sign at the back of the queue.

SWISS FAMILY TREEHOUSE

There is rarely a wait for this walk-through attraction. Look for the following items as you explore the Robinsons' treehouse from the 1960 Disney film.

❶ Find a grinder.

| Team A ⭘ | Team B ⭘ | Team C ⭘ |
| Team D ⭘ | Team E ⭘ | Team F ⭘ |

❷ Find a two-masted schooner.

| Team A ⭘ | Team B ⭘ | Team C ⭘ |
| Team D ⭘ | Team E ⭘ | Team F ⭘ |

❸ Find a telescope.*

| Team A ⭘ | Team B ⭘ | Team C ⭘ |
| Team D ⭘ | Team E ⭘ | Team F ⭘ |

❹ Find a ship's log.

| Team A ⭘ | Team B ⭘ | Team C ⭘ |
| Team D ⭘ | Team E ⭘ | Team F ⭘ |

1. *On a shelf in the living room on the far left.*
2. *On a pitcher in Mr. and Mrs. Robinsons' bedroom.*
3. *In the boys bedroom. Also, two crossed on the family coat of arms.*
4. *On a desk in the library.*

TOM SAWYER ISLAND

*Tom Sawyer Island offers a peaceful respite from the hustle
and bustle of the Magic Kingdom. As you explore the island,
keep an eye out for the items below.*

❶ Find a bluebird in a nest.

Team A ⬭ Team B ⬭ Team C ⬭

Team D ⬭ Team E ⬭ Team F ⬭

❷ Find an owl.

Team A ⬭ Team B ⬭ Team C ⬭

Team D ⬭ Team E ⬭ Team F ⬭

❸ Find a wheelbarrow.*

Team A ⬭ Team B ⬭ Team C ⬭

Team D ⬭ Team E ⬭ Team F ⬭

❹ Find a barrel of lamp oil.

Team A ⬭ Team B ⬭ Team C ⬭

Team D ⬭ Team E ⬭ Team F ⬭

1. *In between the cogs on the horizontal gear in Harper's Mill.*
2. *Inside in the rafters in Harper's Mill.*
3. *Inside the windmill.*
4. *On a dock near the barrel bridge entrance.*

TOMORROWLAND SPEEDWAY

Auto racing scenes and memorabilia highlight this popular attraction. Before jumping in your car to race it around the track, see if you can find the items below as you wait in the queue.

❶ Find a Goodyear tire.

Team A ⭘   Team B ⭘   Team C ⭘

Team D ⭘   Team E ⭘   Team F ⭘

❷ Find two crossed checkered flags.

Team A ⭘   Team B ⭘   Team C ⭘

Team D ⭘   Team E ⭘   Team F ⭘

❸ Find a racetrack in Tokyo.

Team A ⭘   Team B ⭘   Team C ⭘

Team D ⭘   Team E ⭘   Team F ⭘

❹ Find Victory Circle.*

Team A ⭘   Team B ⭘   Team C ⭘

Team D ⭘   Team E ⭘   Team F ⭘

4. Behind the loading area.
3. On the Intergalactic Racing Circuit poster.
2. On a sign in the queue area.
1. In front of the yellow racing car on the raised platform to the left of the queue.

TOMORROWLAND TRANSIT AUTHORITY PEOPLEMOVER

This relaxing ride takes you on a leisurely tour of Tomorrowland. Seek out the items below while enjoying unique views of several area attractions along the way. No waiting required!

1 Find a checkered flag.*

Team A ☐   Team B ☐   Team C ☐

Team D ☐   Team E ☐   Team F ☐

2 Find a robot dog.

Team A ☐   Team B ☐   Team C ☐

Team D ☐   Team E ☐   Team F ☐

3 Find two astronauts.

Team A ☐   Team B ☐   Team C ☐

Team D ☐   Team E ☐   Team F ☐

4 Find a hair salon.

Team A ☐   Team B ☐   Team C ☐

Team D ☐   Team E ☐   Team F ☐

1. *On the Tomorrowland Speedway racetrack.*
2. *In a lower level diorama in Space Mountain.*
3. *Suspended overhead inside Space Mountain.*
4. *On the right before entering Buzz Lightyear's Space Ranger Spin.*

WALT DISNEY'S CAROUSEL OF PROGRESS

As this Disney attraction rarely has a wait, the items in this scavenger hunt can be found on the ride itself. As your theater rotates, look for one item in each of the four different periods of the 20th century.

1 Find a cat.*

Team A ◯   Team B ◯   Team C ◯

Team D ◯   Team E ◯   Team F ◯

2 Find a no parking sign.

Team A ◯   Team B ◯   Team C ◯

Team D ◯   Team E ◯   Team F ◯

3 Find an airplane.

Team A ◯   Team B ◯   Team C ◯

Team D ◯   Team E ◯   Team F ◯

4 Find a Mickey nutcracker.

Team A ◯   Team B ◯   Team C ◯

Team D ◯   Team E ◯   Team F ◯

1. *Look for a quick appearance on a side stage in the first act, Valentine's Day around the beginning of the 20th century.*

2. *You'll see it in the second act, during the Fourth of July in the 1920s.*

3. *Watch closely during the third act, around Halloween in the 1940s.*

4. *You can spot Mickey on the fireplace mantel in the fourth act, around Christmas in the present day.*

TOTAL POINTS

How did you do? Add up all team points from this park and write the totals below!

Team A _____ points

Team B _____ points

Team C _____ points

Team D _____ points

Team E _____ points

Team F _____ points

CHAPTER 3

EPCOT

Epcot was the second park built at the Walt Disney World Resort, opening in 1982. Epcot is an acronym of Experimental Prototype Community of Tomorrow, the name originally given by Walt Disney to a conceptual city of the future that he had wanted to build. The park celebrates human creativity, imagination, and diversity with a focus on international culture and technological innovation.

At 300 acres, Epcot is twice the size of the Magic Kingdom. The park is divided into two lands, Future World and World Showcase, separated by the World Showcase Lagoon. Epcot presents a mix of attractions. Future World features rides and entertainment which focus on technological advancements and innovation, while the pavilions that make up the World Showcase highlight the culture and cuisine of 11 different countries.

Queues in Epcot vary, from traditional winding queues on rides such as Test Track and The Seas with Nemo & Friends, to queue waiting rooms for shows like Captain EO and Turtle Talk with Crush. Unless otherwise noted, all scavenger hunt items in Future World (FW) can be found in or around the queues. Aside from the Maelstrom adventure cruise and Gran Fiesta Tour Starring the Three Caballeros, World Showcase (WS) contains very few traditional queues. To add an additional element of fun to a visit through World Showcase, scavenger hunt items in each country can be found anywhere in the pavilion.

Captain EO (FW)

Captain EO is a 3-D outer space adventure starring Michael Jackson. Scan the waiting area outside the theater for the items below while watching the pre-show documentary on the making of the film.

❶ Find a red cone.

Team A ⬭   Team B ⬭   Team C ⬭

Team D ⬭   Team E ⬭   Team F ⬭

❷ Find an elephant-like creature.*

Team A ⬭   Team B ⬭   Team C ⬭

Team D ⬭   Team E ⬭   Team F ⬭

❸ Find airplanes flying in formation.

Team A ⬭   Team B ⬭   Team C ⬭

Team D ⬭   Team E ⬭   Team F ⬭

❹ Find a pyramid of screens.

Team A ⬭   Team B ⬭   Team C ⬭

Team D ⬭   Team E ⬭   Team F ⬭

1. *At the top of the Captain EO entrance sign at the start of the queue.*
2. *Hooter in the Captain EO poster.*
3. *In the video shown in the queue waiting area.*
4. *The screens over the pre-show queue form a pyramid shape.*

JOURNEY INTO IMAGINATION WITH FIGMENT (FW)

Before journeying into the sensory labs with Figment, you'll have a chance to wander through the brightly-colored Imagination Institute queue. Scan the portraits and award-winning inventions for the following items.

❶ Find a Flying Lab Assistant Robot.

Team A ⬭ Team B ⬭ Team C ⬭
Team D ⬭ Team E ⬭ Team F ⬭

❷ Find a purple telephone.*

Team A ⬭ Team B ⬭ Team C ⬭
Team D ⬭ Team E ⬭ Team F ⬭

❸ Find a megaphone.

Team A ⬭ Team B ⬭ Team C ⬭
Team D ⬭ Team E ⬭ Team F ⬭

❹ Find a color wheel.

Team A ⬭ Team B ⬭ Team C ⬭
Team D ⬭ Team E ⬭ Team F ⬭

4. *Behind a caged enclosure on a shelf in the storage room.*
3. *Behind a caged enclosure on a shelf in the storage room.*
2. *On a desk in the storage room.*
1. *Weebo the robot in a glass display case near the start of the queue.*

LIVING WITH THE LAND (FW)

Living with the Land is located within The Land Pavilion. Its queue features inspirational quotes from world leaders, scientists, philosophers, and writers. These items can all be seen from the queue line and loading area.

❶ Find a Mickey with purple head and blue ears.

Team A ⬭   Team B ⬭   Team C ⬭

Team D ⬭   Team E ⬭   Team F ⬭

❷ Find a scythe.

Team A ⬭   Team B ⬭   Team C ⬭

Team D ⬭   Team E ⬭   Team F ⬭

❸ Find snowflakes.*

Team A ⬭   Team B ⬭   Team C ⬭

Team D ⬭   Team E ⬭   Team F ⬭

❹ Find a quote by a former President.

Team A ⬭   Team B ⬭   Team C ⬭

Team D ⬭   Team E ⬭   Team F ⬭

1. *A classic Hidden Mickey in the lower right area of the mural in the loading area.*
2. *In the mural behind the loading area.*
3. *Hanging from the balloons above the food court.*
4. *In the queue area mural.*

MISSION: SPACE (FW)

Get ready for a mission to Mars! Before boarding your space craft, you'll wind through the International Space Training Center. See if you can spot these items on your tour.

1 Find a moon marker honoring of the Apollo 11 mission.

Team A ◯   Team B ◯   Team C ◯

Team D ◯   Team E ◯   Team F ◯

2 Find a treadmill.

Team A ◯   Team B ◯   Team C ◯

Team D ◯   Team E ◯   Team F ◯

3 Find a Lunar Roving Vehicle.*

Team A ◯   Team B ◯   Team C ◯

Team D ◯   Team E ◯   Team F ◯

4 Find an albatross coming in for a rough landing.

Team A ◯   Team B ◯   Team C ◯

Team D ◯   Team E ◯   Team F ◯

1. *On the large model of the moon immediately after you receive your Launch Ticket.*
2. *In the large, rotating gravity wheel.*
3. *Hanging from the ceiling just before the portrait gallery.*
4. *On the monitors in the Mission Control room.*

THE SEAS WITH NEMO & FRIENDS (FW)

This ride's lengthy queue sets the stage for your under-the-sea adventure. Enjoy a stroll on the beach and boardwalk as you search for the following items.

❶ Find a hammerhead shark.

| Team A ⬭ | Team B ⬭ | Team C ⬭ |
| Team D ⬭ | Team E ⬭ | Team F ⬭ |

❷ Find an octopus.*

| Team A ⬭ | Team B ⬭ | Team C ⬭ |
| Team D ⬭ | Team E ⬭ | Team F ⬭ |

❸ Find a "No Reef Funds" sign.

| Team A ⬭ | Team B ⬭ | Team C ⬭ |
| Team D ⬭ | Team E ⬭ | Team F ⬭ |

❹ Find a boat anchor.

| Team A ⬭ | Team B ⬭ | Team C ⬭ |
| Team D ⬭ | Team E ⬭ | Team F ⬭ |

1. In the *Sharks Sighted!* sign.
2. On the *Welcome to Coral Caves Beach* poster.
3. On the *Darla's Beach Rentals* sign on the life guard station.
4. Hanging from the boat on the ceiling over the queue.

Soarin' (FW)

Soarin' is infamous for its lengthy wait times. When you're not playing one of the new interactive video games, pass the time searching for these items in the Soarin' queue.

❶ Find a red hang glider.

Team A ⬭ Team B ⬭ Team C ⬭
Team D ⬭ Team E ⬭ Team F ⬭

❷ Find a forest.*

Team A ⬭ Team B ⬭ Team C ⬭
Team D ⬭ Team E ⬭ Team F ⬭

❸ Find Concourse 1.

Team A ⬭ Team B ⬭ Team C ⬭
Team D ⬭ Team E ⬭ Team F ⬭

❹ Find a large "X".

Team A ⬭ Team B ⬭ Team C ⬭
Team D ⬭ Team E ⬭ Team F ⬭

1. Over the "o" on the Soarin' sign.
2. On the large video screens in the first section of the queue.
3. On a sign on the wall.
4. Formed by the support beams near the entrance door.

SPACESHIP EARTH (FW)

Queue up outside this giant geodesic dome in preparation for a trip through the history of communication. These items can all be found prior to entering the attraction.

❶ Find red and green Mickey lights.

Team A ◯	Team B ◯	Team C ◯
Team D ◯	Team E ◯	Team F ◯

❷ Find satellite 2350.*

Team A ◯	Team B ◯	Team C ◯
Team D ◯	Team E ◯	Team F ◯

❸ Find a Mickey with blue and yellow ears.

Team A ◯	Team B ◯	Team C ◯
Team D ◯	Team E ◯	Team F ◯

3. *On the sign for The Art of Disney gallery.*
2. *In the mural before entering the geodesic dome.*
1. *In the vegetation around the trees along the left outside queue.*

Test Track (FW)

This automobile testing laboratory queue is LOUD! See if you can spot these items while observing the various safety tests being conducted.

1 Find a Mickey Pez dispenser.

Team A ⬭ Team B ⬭ Team C ⬭

Team D ⬭ Team E ⬭ Team F ⬭

2 Find a broken windshield.*

Team A ⬭ Team B ⬭ Team C ⬭

Team D ⬭ Team E ⬭ Team F ⬭

3 Find a heart wearing a seatbelt.

Team A ⬭ Team B ⬭ Team C ⬭

Team D ⬭ Team E ⬭ Team F ⬭

4 Find a "Crabi" crash test dummy.

Team A ⬭ Team B ⬭ Team C ⬭

Team D ⬭ Team E ⬭ Team F ⬭

1. *In a cup on a red tool cabinet in area 2b.*
2. *Near the Windshield Test Area 6b.*
3. *In the wall of road signs.*
4. *Behind the chain link fence near the loading doors.*

TURTLE TALK WITH CRUSH (FW)

This interactive show features a computer-animated version of the surfer dude turtle from Finding Nemo. Spot these items in the small pre-show waiting area before entering the theater.

1 Find cleaner shrimp.

Team A ◯   Team B ◯   Team C ◯

Team D ◯   Team E ◯   Team F ◯

2 Find a moon jelly.

Team A ◯   Team B ◯   Team C ◯

Team D ◯   Team E ◯   Team F ◯

3 Find a clown fish.*

Team A ◯   Team B ◯   Team C ◯

Team D ◯   Team E ◯   Team F ◯

4 Find a fish with eyes on top of its head.

Team A ◯   Team B ◯   Team C ◯

Team D ◯   Team E ◯   Team F ◯

4.   *A flounder fish in a tank near the entrance.*
3.   *In the tank near the entrance to the theater.*
2.   *In the display on the left wall of the queue.*
1.   *In a tank in the queue.*

AMERICAN ADVENTURE PAVILION (WS)

Explore a slice of Americana in this stately Georgian manor with exhibits celebrating the history and spirit of the United States. Items in this scavenger hunt can be found anywhere in and around the pavilion.

❶ Find a golden eagle.*

Team A ⬭   Team B ⬭   Team C ⬭
Team D ⬭   Team E ⬭   Team F ⬭

❷ Find a quote from Walt Disney.

Team A ⬭   Team B ⬭   Team C ⬭
Team D ⬭   Team E ⬭   Team F ⬭

❸ Find a large wooden ship with sails.

Team A ⬭   Team B ⬭   Team C ⬭
Team D ⬭   Team E ⬭   Team F ⬭

❹ Find the Space Shuttle.

Team A ⬭   Team B ⬭   Team C ⬭
Team D ⬭   Team E ⬭   Team F ⬭

1. On top of the American Adventure sign.
2. On the wall in the rotunda.
3. The recreated 18th century Virginia Sloop Golden Dream is moored behind the stage of the American Gardens Theater.
4. In the painting "Reaching for the Stars" on the wall.

CANADA PAVILION (WS)

From its Native American totems and mountain waterfall to its French chateau and Victoria Gardens, the Canada Pavilion pays tribute to the cultural and geographic diversity of this great country. Look throughout the pavilion to spot these items.

❶ Find Mickey on a totem pole.

Team A ⭕   Team B ⭕   Team C ⭕

Team D ⭕   Team E ⭕   Team F ⭕

❷ Find a pair of snowshoes.*

Team A ⭕   Team B ⭕   Team C ⭕

Team D ⭕   Team E ⭕   Team F ⭕

❸ Find a tin of Cadbury's Cocoa Essence.

Team A ⭕   Team B ⭕   Team C ⭕

Team D ⭕   Team E ⭕   Team F ⭕

❹ Find a wheelbarrow.

Team A ⭕   Team B ⭕   Team C ⭕

Team D ⭕   Team E ⭕   Team F ⭕

1. *The left totem pole has black classic Hidden Mickeys on both sides under the top set of arms.*
2. *Hanging from the front of the Northwest Mercantile.*
3. *On a high shelf inside the Northwest Mercantile.*
4. *Near the waterfall at the back of the pavilion.*

CHINA PAVILION (WS)

Step through the arched ceremonial gate and enter the ancient land of China. Explore the Hall of Prayer, Street of Good Fortune, and an exotic water garden as you search the pavilion. Can you find these items?

❶ Find a lion with a cub under its paw.

Team A ○   Team B ○   Team C ○

Team D ○   Team E ○   Team F ○

❷ Find a crossbow.

Team A ○   Team B ○   Team C ○

Team D ○   Team E ○   Team F ○

❸ Find a folding ruler.

Team A ○   Team B ○   Team C ○

Team D ○   Team E ○   Team F ○

❹ Find an elephant.*

Team A ○   Team B ○   Team C ○

Team D ○   Team E ○   Team F ○

1. *The lion on the left at the gallery entrance.*
2. *On the cart in the Tomb Warriors exhibit.*
3. *In the archeologists display in the Tomb Warriors exhibit.*
4. *The statue on the Street of Good Fortune.*

FRANCE PAVILION (WS)

The architecture, gardens, and artwork of turn-of-the-century France is on display in the France Pavilion. Be sure to search inside and out as you wind your way through the cobblestone streets.

1 Find Remy from the movie Ratatouille.

Team A ⬭   Team B ⬭   Team C ⬭

Team D ⬭   Team E ⬭   Team F ⬭

2 Find a container of six dozen eggs.

Team A ⬭   Team B ⬭   Team C ⬭

Team D ⬭   Team E ⬭   Team F ⬭

3 Find a painting on an easel.

Team A ⬭   Team B ⬭   Team C ⬭

Team D ⬭   Team E ⬭   Team F ⬭

4 Find a paint palette.*

Team A ⬭   Team B ⬭   Team C ⬭

Team D ⬭   Team E ⬭   Team F ⬭

4.   In the mural on the side of Plume et Palette.

3.   Just over the wall on the waterfront near the rowboat.

2.   On a high shelf behind the counter in Boulangerie Patisserie.

1.   Remy is hiding in a basket near the ceiling by the cash register in the wine shop.

GERMANY PAVILION (WS)

Step into a cobblestoned German town platz, complete with a clock tower at the center. Items on this search can be found anywhere in and around the pavilion. Don't forget to search the miniature German village!

❶ Find tiny people kissing.

Team A ◯　　　Team B ◯　　　Team C ◯

Team D ◯　　　Team E ◯　　　Team F ◯

❷ Find a boy and a girl ringing a bell.

Team A ◯　　　Team B ◯　　　Team C ◯

Team D ◯　　　Team E ◯　　　Team F ◯

❸ Find a pickle tree.*

Team A ◯　　　Team B ◯　　　Team C ◯

Team D ◯　　　Team E ◯　　　Team F ◯

❹ Find a nutcracker playing an accordion.

Team A ◯　　　Team B ◯　　　Team C ◯

Team D ◯　　　Team E ◯　　　Team F ◯

1. *In the Model Village and Railroad outside the Germany Pavilion, under the gazebo and in front of the shop.*
2. *When the clock tower at the center of the town comes to life.*
3. *Inside the Die Weihnachts Ecke Christmas shop.*
4. *Overhead inside Der Teddybär Toy Shop.*

ITALY PAVILION (WS)

The romance of Venice comes alive in the Italy Pavilion. Enter St. Mark's Square and explore bridges, towers, and fountains on this Italian scavenger hunt.

1 Find a gondola.

Team A ⬭   Team B ⬭   Team C ⬭

Team D ⬭   Team E ⬭   Team F ⬭

2 Find a bunch of grapes.*

Team A ⬭   Team B ⬭   Team C ⬭

Team D ⬭   Team E ⬭   Team F ⬭

3 Find a knight on horseback.

Team A ⬭   Team B ⬭   Team C ⬭

Team D ⬭   Team E ⬭   Team F ⬭

4 Find a lion holding a book.

Team A ⬭   Team B ⬭   Team C ⬭

Team D ⬭   Team E ⬭   Team F ⬭

4. *In the carving high up on Doge's Palace.*
3. *On the colorful Sicilian donkey cart near the edge of the Italy Pavilion.*
2. *Over the Enoteca Castello wine shop.*
1. *At the lakefront in front of the Italy Pavilion.*

JAPAN PAVILION (WS)

A red Torii gate greets you at the entrance to the Japan Pavilion. This search takes you under the shadow of a five-story pagoda through beautiful tiered gardens in one of the more picturesque countries in the World Showcase.

1 Find Mickey in the water.

Team A ◯   Team B ◯   Team C ◯

Team D ◯   Team E ◯   Team F ◯

2 Find a samurai warrior on a horse.

Team A ◯   Team B ◯   Team C ◯

Team D ◯   Team E ◯   Team F ◯

3 Find a pearl in an oyster.

Team A ◯   Team B ◯   Team C ◯

Team D ◯   Team E ◯   Team F ◯

4 Find Hello Kitty.*

Team A ◯   Team B ◯   Team C ◯

Team D ◯   Team E ◯   Team F ◯

1. *A classic Hidden Mickey is on the drain cover in the Koi pond.*
2. *Two, one on each side, just before the bridge that leads to the Nijo castle.*
3. *Inside the Mitsukoshi department store at the Pick-A-Pearl bar.*
4. *On numerous items inside the Mitsukoshi department store.*

MEXICO PAVILION (WS)

The Mexico Pavilion is housed almost entirely within an enormous Aztec temple. Take a leisurely ride with The Three Caballeros, then explore the bustling Plaza de los Amigos. Conduct your hunt anywhere in and around the pyramid.

❶ Find a stone bird.

Team A ⬭   Team B ⬭   Team C ⬭

Team D ⬭   Team E ⬭   Team F ⬭

❷ Find Mickey in a volcano.

Team A ⬭   Team B ⬭   Team C ⬭

Team D ⬭   Team E ⬭   Team F ⬭

❸ Find a parrot in a cage.*

Team A ⬭   Team B ⬭   Team C ⬭

Team D ⬭   Team E ⬭   Team F ⬭

❹ Find a butterfly piñata.

Team A ⬭   Team B ⬭   Team C ⬭

Team D ⬭   Team E ⬭   Team F ⬭

1. *Across from the pyramid on a ledge over the entrance to the bathroom.*
2. *Every minute or so, holes in the volcano smoke form classic Hidden Mickeys.*
3. *Near the left staircase leading down from the balcony into the market.*
4. *Hanging from the balcony in the Plaza de los Amigos.*

MOROCCO PAVILION (WS)

Enter through the Koutoubia Minaret prayer tower and into the old city to explore a bustling marketplace in the Morocco Pavilion. Search throughout this North African nation's pavilion to find the items below.

❶ Find a water wheel.*

Team A ⬭ Team B ⬭ Team C ⬭

Team D ⬭ Team E ⬭ Team F ⬭

❷ Find Aladdin's Lamp.

Team A ⬭ Team B ⬭ Team C ⬭

Team D ⬭ Team E ⬭ Team F ⬭

❸ Find a small container of poivre (pepper).

Team A ⬭ Team B ⬭ Team C ⬭

Team D ⬭ Team E ⬭ Team F ⬭

❹ Find a chicken on a pot.

Team A ⬭ Team B ⬭ Team C ⬭

Team D ⬭ Team E ⬭ Team F ⬭

4. *The blue pot hanging overhead near Tangier Traders.*

3. *On a shelf inside the Fez house.*

2. *On a rear stage post, and another on the back of the cart, at the Mo' Rockin music stage near the Henna Tattoo area.*

1. *At the lake in front of the Morocco Pavilion.*

NORWAY PAVILION (WS)

The Norway Pavilion contains one of the few rides in the World Showcase, Maelstrom. Search for items in the queue line for this Viking-themed boat ride, then explore the entire Norwegian town square to complete the scavenger hunt.

1 Find a pretzel.*

Team A ◯ Team B ◯ Team C ◯

Team D ◯ Team E ◯ Team F ◯

2 Find a 9th century spearhead.

Team A ◯ Team B ◯ Team C ◯

Team D ◯ Team E ◯ Team F ◯

3 Find a Mickey Mouse watch.

Team A ◯ Team B ◯ Team C ◯

Team D ◯ Team E ◯ Team F ◯

4 Find a viking wearing Mickey ears.

Team A ◯ Team B ◯ Team C ◯

Team D ◯ Team E ◯ Team F ◯

---

1. *Hanging above the entrance to Kringla Bakeri og Kafe.*
2. *In a glass display case inside the Stave Church Gallery.*
3. *In the Maelstrom loading area mural, a construction worker is wearing a Mickey Mouse watch.*
4. *In the Maelstrom loading area mural, the Viking sitting in the boat beneath the middle red stripe of the sail is wearing Mickey ears.*

54

United Kingdom Pavilion (WS)

The cobblestone streets of an old-world English village welcome you at the United Kingdom Pavilion. Search cottages, gardens, and pubs on this search through merry old England.

❶ Find a rose and a crown.*

Team A ⬭   Team B ⬭   Team C ⬭

Team D ⬭   Team E ⬭   Team F ⬭

❷ Find a pot over a fire.

Team A ⬭   Team B ⬭   Team C ⬭

Team D ⬭   Team E ⬭   Team F ⬭

❸ Find a Mickey made out of sports equipment.

Team A ⬭   Team B ⬭   Team C ⬭

Team D ⬭   Team E ⬭   Team F ⬭

❹ Find a white horse.

Team A ⬭   Team B ⬭   Team C ⬭

Team D ⬭   Team E ⬭   Team F ⬭

1. *The Rose & Crown Pub sign.*
2. *In the fireplace inside The Tea Caddy tea shop.*
3. *A sign hanging outside the Sportsmans Shoppe has a classic Hidden Mickey with a tennis racket head and a soccer ball and a rugby ball for ears.*
4. *On the hanging sign for Lords and Ladies Fancy Goods.*

TOTAL POINTS

How did you do? Add up all team points from this park and write the totals below!

Team A   _____ points

Team B   _____ points

Team C   _____ points

Team D   _____ points

Team E   _____ points

Team F   _____ points

CHAPTER 4

HOLLYWOOD STUDIOS

Disney's Hollywood Studios celebrates the glitz and glamour of the entertainment industry. Part amusement park, part working television and motion picture production facility when it first opened in 1989, the park now operates exclusively as a theme park. Hollywood Studios boasts more than 18 rides and attractions as well as live shows and entertainment. Its restaurants are regarded as some of the best in the four Disney theme parks.

Unlike the other three parks in the Walt Disney World Resort, Hollywood Studios does not have a defined layout. Instead, it is comprised of several themed areas - Hollywood Boulevard/Echo Lake, Streets of America/Commissary Lane, Mickey Avenue/Pixar Place, and Sunset Boulevard - that blend into each other, similar to a real motion picture studio.

The scavenger hunts in Hollywood Studios vary greatly, from exquisitely-themed winding queue hunts in rides like The Twilight Zone Tower of Terror and Rock 'n' Roller Coaster Starring Aerosmith, to walk-throughs such as the search in Walt Disney: One Man's Dream. With the abundance of shows at the park, pre-show waiting room searches, like the ones in Muppet Vision 3-D and Voyage of The Little Mermaid, and stage hunts in live performer shows like The American Idol Experience and Lights, Motors, Action! Extreme Stunt Show, are also included.

THE AMERICAN IDOL EXPERIENCE

If you're not performing live on stage, join the voting audience. You may just find the next American Idol! And while you're sitting in the theater waiting for the show to start, see if you can find the items below.

❶ Find Mickey on the arch.

Team A ◯   Team B ◯   Team C ◯

Team D ◯   Team E ◯   Team F ◯

❷ Find a skyscraper.*

Team A ◯   Team B ◯   Team C ◯

Team D ◯   Team E ◯   Team F ◯

❸ Find Dory and Marlin from Finding Nemo.

Team A ◯   Team B ◯   Team C ◯

Team D ◯   Team E ◯   Team F ◯

1. *A classic Hidden Mickey between the second and third lights on the right side of the arch.*
2. *In the video playing behind the stage.*
3. *On a sticker under the big globe on the right side of the stage.*

THE GREAT MOVIE RIDE

The Great Movie Ride is a journey into scenes from some of the most famous movies ever made. All items on this hunt can be found in the courtyard outside the attraction as well as along the inside queue.

1 Find a jingle bell.

Team A ⬭   Team B ⬭   Team C ⬭
Team D ⬭   Team E ⬭   Team F ⬭

2 Find a robot's footprints.

Team A ⬭   Team B ⬭   Team C ⬭
Team D ⬭   Team E ⬭   Team F ⬭

3 Find Kermit the Frog.*

Team A ⬭   Team B ⬭   Team C ⬭
Team D ⬭   Team E ⬭   Team F ⬭

4 Find Mary Poppins' horse.

Team A ⬭   Team B ⬭   Team C ⬭
Team D ⬭   Team E ⬭   Team F ⬭

1. *Around the lion's neck by the entrance door.*
2. *C3PO's footprints in the concrete outside the attraction.*
3. *In the concrete in the courtyard outside the attraction.*
4. *Her carousel horse, in a display case along the inside queue.*

INDIANA JONES EPIC STUNT SPECTACULAR!

You'll feel like you're deep in the jungle on an adventure of your own as you work your way through the Indiana Jones Epic Stunt Spectacular! queue. Search through the brush on both sides of the queue to find the following items.

❶ Find a clipboard with three pencils.

Team A ⬭　　Team B ⬭　　Team C ⬭

Team D ⬭　　Team E ⬭　　Team F ⬭

❷ Find a crate of skeletal remains.

Team A ⬭　　Team B ⬭　　Team C ⬭

Team D ⬭　　Team E ⬭　　Team F ⬭

❸ Find a pair of binoculars.*

Team A ⬭　　Team B ⬭　　Team C ⬭

Team D ⬭　　Team E ⬭　　Team F ⬭

❹ Find the wreckage from an airplane.

Team A ⬭　　Team B ⬭　　Team C ⬭

Team D ⬭　　Team E ⬭　　Team F ⬭

1. *In the right side queue area hanging from an artifacts table.*
2. *In the right side queue area in the brush under a lantern and vessel fragments crate.*
3. *In the right side queue area on a tripod atop a wooden table.*
4. *In the left side queue area in the brush to the left of the trail.*

LIGHTS, MOTORS, ACTION! EXTREME STUNT SHOW

You may feel as if you have stepped onto the French Riviera when you enter Lights, Motors, Action! Extreme Stunt Show. As you sit in the grandstand waiting for the show to begin, scan the set and see if you can spot these items.

❶ Find a surfboard.*

| Team A ⬭ | Team B ⬭ | Team C ⬭ |
| Team D ⬭ | Team E ⬭ | Team F ⬭ |

❷ Find a Weber grill.

| Team A ⬭ | Team B ⬭ | Team C ⬭ |
| Team D ⬭ | Team E ⬭ | Team F ⬭ |

❸ Find a pig.

| Team A ⬭ | Team B ⬭ | Team C ⬭ |
| Team D ⬭ | Team E ⬭ | Team F ⬭ |

❹ Find two arrows pointing left.

| Team A ⬭ | Team B ⬭ | Team C ⬭ |
| Team D ⬭ | Team E ⬭ | Team F ⬭ |

1. In front of Tres Sportiff on the right side of the stage.
2. On the balcony above Pressing Le Coup de Torchon on the left side of the stage.
3. Hanging from a knife over the Boucherie shop above the blue and white striped awning.
4. On top of the buildings to the left and right of center stage.

THE MAGIC OF DISNEY ANIMATION

While there is not much to see in the outside queue, this attraction's small theater stage is full of knick-knacks and Disney paraphernalia. While you're waiting for the show to start, see if you can find these items.

❶ Find a genie in a bottle.*

Team A ⬭   Team B ⬭   Team C ⬭
Team D ⬭   Team E ⬭   Team F ⬭

❷ Find Darth Vader.

Team A ⬭   Team B ⬭   Team C ⬭
Team D ⬭   Team E ⬭   Team F ⬭

❸ Find a group of Pez dispensers.

Team A ⬭   Team B ⬭   Team C ⬭
Team D ⬭   Team E ⬭   Team F ⬭

❹ Find a conch shell.

Team A ⬭   Team B ⬭   Team C ⬭
Team D ⬭   Team E ⬭   Team F ⬭

1. *On the second shelf on the left.*
2. *On top of the file cabinet on the left side of the desk.*
3. *On the middle shelf on the left side of the desk.*
4. *On top of the bookcase on the right.*

MUPPET VISION 3-D

Some visitors feel this attraction's queue is as good as the show itself. Be sure to leave extra time to explore all the gags and props as you wind through Muppet Labs. All items on this hunt can be found before you enter the theater.

❶ Find a crate containing a piano.*

Team A ⬭   Team B ⬭   Team C ⬭
Team D ⬭   Team E ⬭   Team F ⬭

❷ Find a net full of Jell-O (aka Annette Funicello).

Team A ⬭   Team B ⬭   Team C ⬭
Team D ⬭   Team E ⬭   Team F ⬭

❸ Find a boxing glove.

Team A ⬭   Team B ⬭   Team C ⬭
Team D ⬭   Team E ⬭   Team F ⬭

❹ Find a California sticker.

Team A ⬭   Team B ⬭   Team C ⬭
Team D ⬭   Team E ⬭   Team F ⬭

4. *In a collection of stickers on a black trunk on the left side of the pre-show area.*
3. *Hanging from the ceiling near the back of the pre-show area.*
2. *Green and orange boxes in a net hanging overhead.*
1. *Large crate on the left side of the pre-show area.*

ROCK 'N' ROLLER COASTER STARRING AEROSMITH

This hunt takes place in the attraction's inside queue which winds through a record label office into a recording session with Aerosmith. Then it's off to the alley out back to catch a stretch limo to the concert!

❶ Find a giant G-Force record.*

Team A ⃝   Team B ⃝   Team C ⃝

Team D ⃝   Team E ⃝   Team F ⃝

❷ Find a cat with nine lives.

Team A ⃝   Team B ⃝   Team C ⃝

Team D ⃝   Team E ⃝   Team F ⃝

❸ Find a classic Mickey made with cables.

Team A ⃝   Team B ⃝   Team C ⃝

Team D ⃝   Team E ⃝   Team F ⃝

❹ Find a a sign for Wash This Way Auto Detail.

Team A ⃝   Team B ⃝   Team C ⃝

Team D ⃝   Team E ⃝   Team F ⃝

1. *On the ceiling of the first room in the indoor queue.*
2. *On the drum set in Aerosmith's recording studio.*
3. *A classic Hidden Mickey made from guitar cables can been seen on the floor in front of a guitar rack in Aerosmith's recording studio.*
4. *In a glass case in the alley loading area.*

STAR TOURS

The Star Tours experience begins in the queue where you are immediately immersed in the Star Wars universe. Spot the items below as you wind your way through the spaceport in preparation for a flight to a galaxy far, far away.

❶ Find Mickey on a tree.

Team A ⬭   Team B ⬭   Team C ⬭
Team D ⬭   Team E ⬭   Team F ⬭

❷ Find R2D2 with Mickey Mouse ears.

Team A ⬭   Team B ⬭   Team C ⬭
Team D ⬭   Team E ⬭   Team F ⬭

❸ Find Mickey Mouse in a suitcase.

Team A ⬭   Team B ⬭   Team C ⬭
Team D ⬭   Team E ⬭   Team F ⬭

❹ Find a defective robot.*

Team A ⬭   Team B ⬭   Team C ⬭
Team D ⬭   Team E ⬭   Team F ⬭

4. *On the left side of the queue shortly before the boarding area.*
3. *Inside one of the pieces of luggage in the x-ray machine.*
2. *As one of the silhouettes in the screen near the luggage inspection area.*
1. *A classic Hidden Mickey high on a tree trunk just below the walkway platform for the Ewok village.*

STUDIO BACKLOT TOUR

Although filming rarely occurs here, this tour is still an interesting look at the art of movie making and special effects. Hunt for these items among the movie memorabilia and props in the queue line before boarding the tram.

❶ Find an angel holding a dove.

Team A ⬭ Team B ⬭ Team C ⬭

Team D ⬭ Team E ⬭ Team F ⬭

❷ Find a pig.*

Team A ⬭ Team B ⬭ Team C ⬭

Team D ⬭ Team E ⬭ Team F ⬭

❸ Find Mickey's shoes.

Team A ⬭ Team B ⬭ Team C ⬭

Team D ⬭ Team E ⬭ Team F ⬭

❹ Find a silver Mickey.

Team A ⬭ Team B ⬭ Team C ⬭

Team D ⬭ Team E ⬭ Team F ⬭

1. *The Black Pearl sailing ship figurehead from Pirates of the Caribbean at the beginning of the queue.*
2. *Above the Park Avenue sign in the Prop Room.*
3. *In the first aisle in the Prop Building on the left.*
4. *In the Prop Building, a silver classic Hidden Mickey on a yellow refrigerator.*

TOY STORY MANIA!

This featured attraction at Pixar Place includes an elaborate queue inside Andy's toy box. Look for these items as you wind your way around giant toys, game boards, crayons, and puzzle pieces.

❶ Find a Woody yo-yo.*

Team A ⬭　　Team B ⬭　　Team C ⬭

Team D ⬭　　Team E ⬭　　Team F ⬭

❷ Find Peter Pan teaching the Darling children how to fly.

Team A ⬭　　Team B ⬭　　Team C ⬭

Team D ⬭　　Team E ⬭　　Team F ⬭

❸ Find a lifeguard.

Team A ⬭　　Team B ⬭　　Team C ⬭

Team D ⬭　　Team E ⬭　　Team F ⬭

❹ Find a boy with a slingshot.

Team A ⬭　　Team B ⬭　　Team C ⬭

Team D ⬭　　Team E ⬭　　Team F ⬭

1.　*Over the entrance to the attraction.*

2.　*In one of the frames of the View-Master disc.*

3.　*On the inside face of one of the cards along the left wall of the queue.*

4.　*On the ceiling in the Chutes and Ladders game.*

THE TWILIGHT ZONE TOWER OF TERROR

This queue search begins as you enter the hotel through the main entrance gate. The lengthy line take you through the abandoned Hollywood Tower Hotel down to the eerie boiler room for a ride on its phantom elevator.

❶ Find a pair of eyeglasses.

Team A ◯   Team B ◯   Team C ◯

Team D ◯   Team E ◯   Team F ◯

❷ Find a newspaper.*

Team A ◯   Team B ◯   Team C ◯

Team D ◯   Team E ◯   Team F ◯

❸ Find a cannon.

Team A ◯   Team B ◯   Team C ◯

Team D ◯   Team E ◯   Team F ◯

❹ Find a wrench.

Team A ◯   Team B ◯   Team C ◯

Team D ◯   Team E ◯   Team F ◯

1. On the Concierge desk.
2. On the check-in desk next to the coat and hat.
3. On a table in the library where the video plays.
4. On the boiler room floor.

VOYAGE OF THE LITTLE MERMAID

This 15-minute show, featuring puppets and live actors, recreates the 1989 film The Little Mermaid. As you wait to enter the theater, see if you can find the following items among the various artifacts in the pre-show waiting area.

❶ Find a gas pump handle.

Team A ⬭　　Team B ⬭　　Team C ⬭

Team D ⬭　　Team E ⬭　　Team F ⬭

❷ Find a candle that was once inside a whale.

Team A ⬭　　Team B ⬭　　Team C ⬭

Team D ⬭　　Team E ⬭　　Team F ⬭

❸ Find Ernest Hemingway's fishing pole.*

Team A ⬭　　Team B ⬭　　Team C ⬭

Team D ⬭　　Team E ⬭　　Team F ⬭

❹ Find a typewriter.

Team A ⬭　　Team B ⬭　　Team C ⬭

Team D ⬭　　Team E ⬭　　Team F ⬭

1. *On a wall shelf left of the entrance doors.*
2. *Geppetto's candle found in Monstro.*
3. *Over the entrance doors by the mermaid monkey.*
4. *On the wall next to the left entrance doors.*

WALT DISNEY: ONE MAN'S DREAM

This self-guided tour opened in October 2001 as part of the 100 Years of Magic celebration. You'll find the items below among the exhibits of photographs, audio interviews, and memorabilia that tell the story of Walt Disney.

❶ Find a bottle of blue ink.

Team A ⬭   Team B ⬭   Team C ⬭

Team D ⬭   Team E ⬭   Team F ⬭

❷ Find a Donald Duck jack-in-the-box.

Team A ⬭   Team B ⬭   Team C ⬭

Team D ⬭   Team E ⬭   Team F ⬭

❸ Find an early model of It's a Small World.

Team A ⬭   Team B ⬭   Team C ⬭

Team D ⬭   Team E ⬭   Team F ⬭

❹ Find WALL-E.*

Team A ⬭   Team B ⬭   Team C ⬭

Team D ⬭   Team E ⬭   Team F ⬭

4. In the D23 display at the back of the walk-through near the theater doors.
3. On the desk behind the life-size audio-animatronic of Abraham Lincoln.
2. In the Donald Duck Toys 1934-1936 display.
1. On the animation table used for early Mickey Mouse cartoons.

TOTAL POINTS

How did you do? Add up all team points from this park and write the totals below!

Team A _____ points

Team B _____ points

Team C _____ points

Team D _____ points

Team E _____ points

Team F _____ points

CHAPTER 5

ANIMAL KINGDOM

Nature and conservation is the focus at Disney's Animal Kingdom. The park is home to more than 1,700 animals. Covering 5,000 acres, it is the largest animal-themed park in the world. The park offers a diverse number of attractions, from carnival-like thrill rides to 3-D movies and live stage shows. Its primary draw, however, is its myriad of trails and nature exhibits offering opportunities to get close to the animals and celebrate the conservation of our natural world.

Located in the center of Disney's Animal Kingdom, Discovery Island features the fourteen-story Tree of Life, the park's icon. A system of trails weaves around the massive sculpture, affording unobstructed views of the 325 animals carved into its trunk. Discovery Island is the gateway to all the other areas in the park. Paths lead over the Discovery River waterway to The Oasis, Africa, Asia, Camp Minnie-Mickey, and Dinoland, U.S.A.

Several traditional queue scavenger hunts have been created in Disney's Animal Kingdom. DINOSAUR, Expedition Everest, Kali River Rapids, Kilimanjaro Safaris, Primeval Whirl, and TriceraTop Spin all have traditional winding queues offering plenty of wait time to search for items. Highlighting Animal Kingdom's focus on nature and conservation, scavenger hunts can also be found in the winding trails and open nature exhibits along the Cretaceous Trail, Discovery Island Trails, Maharajah Jungle Trek, and Pangani Forest Exploration Trail.

THE BONEYARD

This dinosaur-themed play area includes a rope climbing structure, slides, caves, and an area where young paleontologists can dig for fossils. You won't need to dig to find the items below, but you will have to look carefully!

❶ Find Mickey on the ground.

Team A ⬭   Team B ⬭   Team C ⬭

Team D ⬭   Team E ⬭   Team F ⬭

❷ Find a drill.

Team A ⬭   Team B ⬭   Team C ⬭

Team D ⬭   Team E ⬭   Team F ⬭

❸ Find a dog dish.

Team A ⬭   Team B ⬭   Team C ⬭

Team D ⬭   Team E ⬭   Team F ⬭

❹ Find a wheelbarrow.*

Team A ⬭   Team B ⬭   Team C ⬭

Team D ⬭   Team E ⬭   Team F ⬭

1. *A classic Hidden Mickey in the darker foam under the water fountain just inside the entrance.*
2. *Hanging on the wall in a fenced-off area on the first level near the stairs.*
3. *Behind the table and chairs in a fenced-off area at the back of the second level by the slides.*
4. *Inside a fenced-off area at the back of the dig site.*

CRETACEOUS TRAIL

This quiet little footpath hides some big secrets! Spot these items as you stroll through a prehistoric garden past fossil dig sites. What was that sound?

1 Find Mickey on a dinosaur.

Team A ◯　　　Team B ◯　　　Team C ◯

Team D ◯　　　Team E ◯　　　Team F ◯

2 Find a trowel.

Team A ◯　　　Team B ◯　　　Team C ◯

Team D ◯　　　Team E ◯　　　Team F ◯

3 Find a dinosaur footprint.*

Team A ◯　　　Team B ◯　　　Team C ◯

Team D ◯　　　Team E ◯　　　Team F ◯

1. *A classic Hidden Mickey made by three dark spots on the back on the large hadrosaurus at the start of the trail.*

2. *On the ground in the brush next to a dinosaur fossil.*

3. *Several, in the walkway along the trail.*

DINOSAUR

Go back in time to when the dinosaurs roamed the planet. Spot these items as you pass through the Dino Institute's museum displays before boarding your Time Rover transport in the secret underground research facility.

1 Find a crayfish.

Team A ⬭ Team B ⬭ Team C ⬭
Team D ⬭ Team E ⬭ Team F ⬭

2 Find Mickey in a tree.

Team A ⬭ Team B ⬭ Team C ⬭
Team D ⬭ Team E ⬭ Team F ⬭

3 Find a microscope.*

Team A ⬭ Team B ⬭ Team C ⬭
Team D ⬭ Team E ⬭ Team F ⬭

4 Find a skull and crossbones.

Team A ⬭ Team B ⬭ Team C ⬭
Team D ⬭ Team E ⬭ Team F ⬭

1. *In a diorama in the Dino Institute Discover Center.*
2. *A classic Hidden Mickey painted on the trunk of a tree in a mural just inside the building entrance on the right side of the queue.*
3. *In the Dino Institute plaque on the wall.*
4. *On a warning sign in the boarding area.*

DISCOVERY ISLAND TRAILS

This series of trails winds around the base of the Tree of Life at the center of Disney's Animal Kingdom. Can you spot these animals among the 325 carved into it's massive trunk?

❶ Find a tiger.*

Team A ⬭   Team B ⬭   Team C ⬭
Team D ⬭   Team E ⬭   Team F ⬭

❷ Find a koala bear.

Team A ⬭   Team B ⬭   Team C ⬭
Team D ⬭   Team E ⬭   Team F ⬭

❸ Find a sea turtle.

Team A ⬭   Team B ⬭   Team C ⬭
Team D ⬭   Team E ⬭   Team F ⬭

❹ Find a shark.

Team A ⬭   Team B ⬭   Team C ⬭
Team D ⬭   Team E ⬭   Team F ⬭

1. *The tiger can be found around the front side of the tree, bottom left.*
2. *The koala bear can be found around the front side of the tree, top right.*
3. *The sea turtle can be found along a trail around the back side of the tree.*
4. *The shark can be found around the back side of the tree, top middle.*

EXPEDITION EVEREST

This attraction has some of the best theming in all of Disney World. The search takes place in the queue, which immerses you in Nepalese history and culture as you wait to board an old steam train for a trip to the top of Everest.

❶ Find a Mouseketeer Mountaineer Expedition patch.

Team A ⬭   Team B ⬭   Team C ⬭

Team D ⬭   Team E ⬭   Team F ⬭

❷ Find a Yeti doll with Mickey ears.

Team A ⬭   Team B ⬭   Team C ⬭

Team D ⬭   Team E ⬭   Team F ⬭

❸ Find tiger scat.*

Team A ⬭   Team B ⬭   Team C ⬭

Team D ⬭   Team E ⬭   Team F ⬭

❹ Find Mickey on a tea kettle.

Team A ⬭   Team B ⬭   Team C ⬭

Team D ⬭   Team E ⬭   Team F ⬭

---

1. On the wall in the Himalayan Escapes booking office.
2. In the cupboards in Tashi's Trek and Tongba Shop, on your right just before exiting.
3. In the Documenting Bio-diversity display near the end of the queue.
4. A classic Hidden Mickey on a dented kettle in the Yeti Museum, on the second table in the destroyed campsite.

It's Tough to be a Bug!

Inspired by the Pixar film A Bug's Life, this 3-D movie is presented in the Tree of Life Theater. Look for the following items along the queue trail leading to the entrance and in the waiting area inside the roots of the massive tree.

❶ Find an elephant.*

Team A ◯   Team B ◯   Team C ◯

Team D ◯   Team E ◯   Team F ◯

❷ Find a horse.

Team A ◯   Team B ◯   Team C ◯

Team D ◯   Team E ◯   Team F ◯

❸ Find a plaque honoring Jane Goodall.

Team A ◯   Team B ◯   Team C ◯

Team D ◯   Team E ◯   Team F ◯

❹ Find a giant dung ball.

Team A ◯   Team B ◯   Team C ◯

Team D ◯   Team E ◯   Team F ◯

1. *Along the outside queue trail.*
2. *Along the outside queue trail.*
3. *In the roots near the Tough to Be a Bug entrance.*
4. *In the inside queue near the theater doors.*

KALI RIVER RAPIDS

It can be a long wait for this wild raft ride down the Chakra-nadi River. Pass the time by searching for these items in the attraction's exquisite Asian-themed queue.

❶ Find a stone monkey.

Team A ⬭　　　Team B ⬭　　　Team C ⬭

Team D ⬭　　　Team E ⬭　　　Team F ⬭

❷ Find a rocking horse.*

Team A ⬭　　　Team B ⬭　　　Team C ⬭

Team D ⬭　　　Team E ⬭　　　Team F ⬭

❸ Find a sleeping cot.

Team A ⬭　　　Team B ⬭　　　Team C ⬭

Team D ⬭　　　Team E ⬭　　　Team F ⬭

❹ Find a black, three-wheeled auto rickshaw.

Team A ⬭　　　Team B ⬭　　　Team C ⬭

Team D ⬭　　　Team E ⬭　　　Team F ⬭

4. On a shelf below the Durgas Delight mural in the inside queue.

3. At the top of the stairs in Mr. Panika's Shop.

2. In the Panika family's backyard.

1. Beyond the bamboo fence on the right side of the outside queue near a set of stairs.

KILIMANJARO SAFARIS

Tours of the Harambe Wildlife Reserve are very popular. As you head down to the Kilimanjaro Safaris departure station to board one of their open-sided safari vehicles, see if you can spot these items.

1 Find the Swahili word for giraffe.

Team A ⬭   Team B ⬭   Team C ⬭
Team D ⬭   Team E ⬭   Team F ⬭

2 Find a 200 shilling note.

Team A ⬭   Team B ⬭   Team C ⬭
Team D ⬭   Team E ⬭   Team F ⬭

3 Find a clay pot.

Team A ⬭   Team B ⬭   Team C ⬭
Team D ⬭   Team E ⬭   Team F ⬭

4 Find a poaching alert sign.*

Team A ⬭   Team B ⬭   Team C ⬭
Team D ⬭   Team E ⬭   Team F ⬭

4. *On a wall near the end of the queue.*
3. *In the rafters overhead in the covered queue.*
2. *Framed over the desk in the Booking Office.*
1. *Twiga, located on a sign overhead at the beginning of the queue.*

MAHARAJAH JUNGLE TREK

Search through the ancient ruins of Anandapur's royal past. All items in this scavenger hunt can be found along the Maharajah Jungle Trek.

❶ Find a photo of men riding elephants.

Team A ○	Team B ○	Team C ○
Team D ○	Team E ○	Team F ○

❷ Find a man wearing a Mickey earring.

Team A ○	Team B ○	Team C ○
Team D ○	Team E ○	Team F ○

❸ Find Mickey in the clouds.

Team A ○	Team B ○	Team C ○
Team D ○	Team E ○	Team F ○

❹ Find a wooden mallet.*

Team A ○	Team B ○	Team C ○
Team D ○	Team E ○	Team F ○

1. *On a bulletin board inside the bat house.*
2. *In the first mural on the left at the second tiger viewing area.*
3. *A classic Hidden Mickey is inside the second arch of the temple ruins, in the mural on the right.*
4. *Hanging on the wall near the prayer flags.*

PANGANI FOREST EXPLORATION TRAIL

This self-guided walking path winds through a wildlife sanctuary and research facility deep in the Harambe Wildlife Reserve. Look for the items below along the densely forested Pangani Forest Exploration Trail.

1 Find a coffee pot.

Team A ⬭   Team B ⬭   Team C ⬭

Team D ⬭   Team E ⬭   Team F ⬭

2 Find a letter to Pangani's Dr. Kulunda from the head of the Ituri Okapi Project, Igwe Olugu.

Team A ⬭   Team B ⬭   Team C ⬭

Team D ⬭   Team E ⬭   Team F ⬭

3 Find a can of Doom bug spray.

Team A ⬭   Team B ⬭   Team C ⬭

Team D ⬭   Team E ⬭   Team F ⬭

4 Find a tiny meerkat skull.*

Team A ⬭   Team B ⬭   Team C ⬭

Team D ⬭   Team E ⬭   Team F ⬭

4. *On a table at the overlook.*
3. *On Dr. Kulunda's desk in the Research Centre.*
2. *On a display board at the observation blind.*
1. *On a shelf in the Endangered Animal Rehabilitation Centre.*

PRIMEVAL WHIRL & TRICERATOP SPIN

Both of these carnival ride queues overlook Chester and Hester's Dino-Rama, a special area within DinoLand, U.S.A. Can you spot the items below?

❶ Find an old Florida license plate.*

Team A ⭘	Team B ⭘	Team C ⭘
Team D ⭘	Team E ⭘	Team F ⭘

❷ Find a windmill.

Team A ⭘	Team B ⭘	Team C ⭘
Team D ⭘	Team E ⭘	Team F ⭘

❸ Find a car muffler.

Team A ⭘	Team B ⭘	Team C ⭘
Team D ⭘	Team E ⭘	Team F ⭘

❹ Find Mickey in a meteor.

Team A ⭘	Team B ⭘	Team C ⭘
Team D ⭘	Team E ⭘	Team F ⭘

1. *Over the Souvenir Photos shelter.*
2. *Two, as weathervanes, on top of Chester and Hester's Dinosaur Treasures shop.*
3. *On the wall under the erupting volcano sign.*
4. *Classic Hidden Mickeys can be found in several meteors on Primeval Whirl.*

WILDLIFE EXPRESS TRAIN TO RAFIKI'S CONSERVATION STATION

The Wildlife Express Train connects Africa to Rafiki's Planet Watch. As you wait to board, look for these items in the Harambe Railway Station.

1 Find a notice of interruption to service to Bwanga Station due to erosion.

Team A ◯   Team B ◯   Team C ◯

Team D ◯   Team E ◯   Team F ◯

2 Find a pair of hiking boots.

Team A ◯   Team B ◯   Team C ◯

Team D ◯   Team E ◯   Team F ◯

3 Find a funnel.

Team A ◯   Team B ◯   Team C ◯

Team D ◯   Team E ◯   Team F ◯

4 Find a bicycle.*

Team A ◯   Team B ◯   Team C ◯

Team D ◯   Team E ◯   Team F ◯

1. *Posted between the two windows of the Booking Office.*
2. *On a stack of luggage near the loading area.*
3. *On top of a crate of survey equipment near the loading area.*
4. *One located near the luggage in the loading area, and another strapped to the front of the train.*

TOTAL POINTS

How did you do? Add up all team points from this park and write the totals below!

Team A   _____ points

Team B   _____ points

Team C   _____ points

Team D   _____ points

Team E   _____ points

Team F   _____ points

CHAPTER 6

SCORING

After visiting your last theme park, it's time to tally the final scores. Use the form below to add up the points for each park, then record the grand totals and crown the winner!

FINAL TEAM SCORES

Team A

MK _____ points

EP _____ points

HS _____ points

AK _____ points

_____ TOTAL

Team B

MK _____ points

EP _____ points

HS _____ points

AK _____ points

_____ TOTAL

Team C

MK _____ points

EP _____ points

HS _____ points

AK _____ points

_____ TOTAL

Team D

MK _____ points

EP _____ points

HS _____ points

AK _____ points

_____ TOTAL

Team E

MK _____ points

EP _____ points

HS _____ points

AK _____ points

_____ TOTAL

Team F

MK _____ points

EP _____ points

HS _____ points

AK _____ points

_____ TOTAL

CONCLUSION

Congratulations on completing your scavenger hunt around Walt Disney World. We hope this queue line challenge helped make the inevitable wait time at Disney theme park attractions a more enjoyable experience.

Since Disney is constantly updating and renovating their attractions, including the queues, it's possible some items have changed since publication. We strive to keep our guides as up-to-date and accurate as possible. If you have any comments or suggestions, we would love to hear from you! Contact us at http://scavengerguides.com.

Scavenger hunts are an exciting way to add an additional level of fun to your vacations. Now that you have had a chance to participate in The Disney World Queue Line Scavenger Hunt, you may be eager to try another. If you enjoyed this activity, check out our interactive guides to other destinations like Washington, DC, New York, and Chicago.

Visit http://scavengerguides.com to learn more.

ABOUT THE AUTHOR

Daniel Ireland's first glimpse at Disney World came as a young boy on a summer vacation with his parents and three siblings. In the years since, he has returned many times, most recently sharing the magic with his own family.

The Disney World Queue Line Scavenger Hunt was a collaborative effort. On their most recent visit, Daniel, his wife Nancy, and children Megan and Andrew passed the time in the long queue lines searching for items to include in this book. They hope you have as much fun participating in the scavenger hunt as they had creating it.

Made in the USA
San Bernardino, CA
22 December 2013